English
made easy

Key Stage 2
ages 7–8

Author
John Hesk

LONDON • NEW YORK • MUNICH • MELBOURNE • DELHI

Prefixes

Can you reassemble the words below by adding a **prefix** to each **root word**? D

Remember: A **prefix** is a group of letters added to the beginning of a word to change its meaning.

ex-   mis-   co-   non-   anti-

take   ordinate

freeze

lead   change   behave

port   clockwise

place   fiction   tend

operate

mis- ..misbehave,..

non- ....

ex- ....

co- ....

anti- ....

Can you make any more words by using the same **prefixes** with different **root words**? D

....

....

....

Remember: Add any new words to your **word bank**.

2

Writing a shape poem

Here is a **shape poem**.

The
Fir Tree is
Standing proud
In
The wild, wintry wood.
Its branches heavily laden with
The soft, white, freshly fallen snow.
Its
Brave deep-green needles blunted by icicles
That add their own sharp, crisp burden
To
Carry.

Try writing your own tree **shape poem** here. It can be about any type of tree you wish. You can use some of the words from the fir-tree **poem**, but try to think of some of your own as well.

....

....

....

....

....

....

....

....

....

Homophones

Use a dictionary to find the definition of each of the **homophones** below.
Then use each **homophone** in a separate sentence. D

Remember: Homophones are words that sound the same but have
a different meaning and sometimes a different spelling.

pair ....

pear ....

pare ....

write ....

right ....

bear ....

bare ....

read ....

reed ....

to ....

too ....

two ....

Remember: Add any new words to your **word bank**.

Multiple meanings

Here is a word that has at least three **meanings**.

> **wave** means: a gesture
> to sway
> a moving ridge of water

Find one word, or **homograph**, to fit the three **meanings** in each group.

Remember: A **homograph** is a word with the same **spelling** as another word but with a different meaning.

opposite of left
correct
a true claim ....

without a pattern
a flat piece of land
easily understood ....

a small sticker on a letter
a mark
to bring down your foot hard ....

a group with members
a caveman's weapon
a type of playing card ....

part of a dress that trails along
to teach
a form of transport ....

a long-legged bird
to stretch to see
a lifting machine ....

a game ending in a tie
to make pictures
to attract ....

a tool for opening doors
a list of map symbols
a scale of musical notes ....

Using a dictionary

The **dictionary** tells you:
- a word's **meaning**
- how the word is **used** (*n.* = noun, *adj.* = adjective, *v.* = verb)
- the **origins** of the word (where it comes from)

All this information helps you remember how a word is spelt.

Look up the words below in your **dictionary**. Give as much information as you can about each word's **meanings**, **uses** and **origins**. D

act

meanings: ....

uses: ....

origins: ....

boom

meanings: ....

uses: ....

origins: ....

comic

meanings: ....

uses: ....

origins: ....

dart

meanings: ....

uses: ....

origins: ....

electric

meanings: ....

uses: ....

origins: ....

Using a dictionary

To make it easier to find a single word in a big **dictionary**, think of the book as being divided into four **quarters**, like this:

First quarter: A, B, C, D, E, F

Second quarter: G, H, I, J, K, L, M

Third quarter: N, O, P, Q, R, S

Fourth quarter: ....

Did you notice any words amongst the scrambled letters on page 4? There are ten words for you to find. Make a list of these words and where they belong in the **dictionary** – in the first, second, third or fourth **quarter**?

vole   fourth quarter

....

....

....

....

....

....

....

....

Remember: Add any new words to your **word bank**.

Alphabetical order

List the words below in **alphabetical order**. Then write down their **meanings, uses** and **origins**. You will need to continue on page 9. D

quack   yarn   zip   part   sandwich

watch   rear   unit   note   xylophone

object   tank   volume

.............*note*...............   meanings: ....

                             uses: ....

                           origins: ....

....   meanings: ....

                             uses: ....

                           origins: ....

....   meanings: ....

                             uses: ....

                           origins: ....

....   meanings: ....

                             uses: ....

                           origins: ....

....   meanings: ....

                             uses: ....

                           origins: ....

....   meanings: ....

                             uses: ....

                           origins: ....

.... meanings: ....

                    uses: ....

                origins: ....

.... meanings: ....

                    uses: ....

                origins: ....

.... meanings: ....

                    uses: ....

                origins: ....

.... meanings: ....

                    uses: ....

                origins: ....

.... meanings: ....

                    uses: ....

                origins: ....

.... meanings: ....

                    uses: ....

                origins: ....

.... zip .... meanings: ....

                    uses: ....

                origins: ....

Writing about talking

Read this extract from the **legend** *King Arthur.* The brave King Arthur has been badly wounded. He wants the knight Bedivere to help him.

They took Arthur inside and laid him down to rest.

"Bedivere," rasped the king, "take my sword, Excalibur. Throw it into the lake. Then come back and tell me what you have seen."

Bedivere took Excalibur. Never in his life had he held such an exquisite sword. He could not bear to throw away such a treasure, so he hid it under a tree, then hurried back to Arthur.

"Did you do it?" Arthur asked him.

"I did, sir."

"And what did you see?"

"Nothing but the waves and the wind, my lord."

"Then you have lied to me!" cried Arthur. "Do as I commanded."

Bedivere went back to the lake. Again he admired Excalibur's unearthly beauty, again he hid it, again he lied to his king.

Arthur was growing weaker. "By Heaven," he gasped, "if you do not obey, there will be no future ...." He could speak no more.

Bedivere was moved by the mystery of his words. Without a word he strode back to the lake shore. This time he took Excalibur and threw it with all his strength, out into the middle of the lake.

At once, a hand rose out of the swirling waters, caught the sword, and brandished it three times. Then, out of the mist, silken voices began to chant:

"Bring him for healing, Over the water!"

Bedivere shivered. He turned and ran back to his wounded lord.

"Quick!" he called to Sir Lucan. "We must fetch the king!"

From *King Arthur,* retold by Rosalind Kerven

The writer has not used the word **said** once. Instead, she has chosen more interesting words. Find these words, and write them here.

....

....

List some other words that could be used instead of the following words. D T

said ....

asked ....

A mysterious story poem

Read this **poem** aloud.

The Listeners

"Is there anybody there?" said the Traveller,
　　Knocking on the moonlit door;
And his horse in the silence champed the grasses
　　Of the forest's ferny floor:
And a bird flew up out of the turret,
　　Above the Traveller's head:
And he smote upon the door again a second time;
　　"Is there anybody there?" he said.
But no one descended to the Traveller;
　　No head from the leaf-fringed sill
Leaned over and looked into his grey eyes,
　　Where he stood perplexed and still.
But only a host of phantom listeners
　　That dwelt in the lone house then
Stood listening in the quiet of the moonlight
　　To that voice from the world of men:
Stood thronging the faint moonbeams on the dark stair,
　　That goes down to the empty hall,
Hearkening in an air stirred and shaken
　　By the lonely Traveller's call.

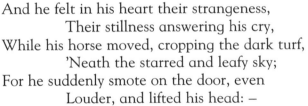

And he felt in his heart their strangeness,
　　Their stillness answering his cry,
While his horse moved, cropping the dark turf,
　　'Neath the starred and leafy sky;
For he suddenly smote on the door, even
　　Louder, and lifted his head: –
"Tell them I came, and no one answered,
　　That I kept my word," he said.
Never the least stir made the listeners,
　　Though every word he spake
Fell echoing through the shadowiness of the still house
　　From the one man left awake:
Ay, they heard his foot upon the stirrup,
　　And the sound of iron on stone,
And how the silence surged softly backward,
　　When the plunging hoofs were gone.

Walter de la Mare

This **poem** seems to be part of a longer mystery story. Why is it mysterious?

....

....

....

11

Understanding the poem

Answer these questions about the **poem** called *The Listeners* on page 11.

Where does this part of the story happen?

....

When does it happen (day or night)? Which words tell you this?

....

....

In your opinion, who or what are "The Listeners"?

....

....

The Traveller speaks in this **poem**. What are his words?

....

....

How does the first line of the **poem** make you feel?

....

....

What do you notice about the sounds in the third and fourth lines,
*And his horse in the silence champed the grasses
Of the forest's ferny floor*
and what does this tell you about the horse's behaviour?

....

....

Make a list of the **adjectives** that are used to describe the Traveller.
Remember: An **adjective** is a describing word.

....

....

Understanding the poem

Answer these further questions about the **poem** on page 11.

Find the meanings of the old-fashioned words in the **poem**. Then write down why you think the poet chose these words. D

....

....

....

Read the **poem** again, looking at the lines and listening for the **rhymes**. How would you describe the **rhyming pattern**?

....

....

Count the **syllables** in the first eight lines – can you find a **rhythmic pattern**? What is it?
Remember: A **syllable** is a word or part of a word that is one beat long.

....

....

Writing practice
Choose a section from the **poem** and write it here.
Remember: Join your letters carefully and space your words evenly.
Begin new lines in the same places as in the printed **poem**.

....

....

....

....

....

....

....

Pronouns

Pronouns are used instead of **nouns** to avoid repeating the **nouns** themselves. Read the following text, which has no **pronouns** in it.

The Traveller arrived at the door. The Traveller knocked on the door, but there was no answer, so the Traveller knocked again. Meanwhile, the Traveller's horse was grazing. The Traveller's horse seemed untroubled.

With **pronouns**, the text becomes much less repetitive.

The Traveller arrived at the door. **He** knocked on **it**, but there was no answer, so **he** knocked again. Meanwhile, **his** horse was grazing. **It** seemed untroubled.

Go back to the **poem** on page 11, and underline all the **pronouns** you can find.

Rewrite the following sentences changing the **nouns** in bold type to **pronouns**.

The Traveller rode **the Traveller's** horse as fast as **the horse** could go.

....

....

Emma said that **Emma** wanted to read **Emma's** favourite poem to them.

....

....

Jack and Kate enjoyed the poem that **Emma** read to **Jack and Kate**.

....

....

Conjunctions

Conjunctions are words that join sentences. Choose one **conjunction** from the list below to join each pair of sentences. Use a different **conjunction** each time.

if   so   while   although   because   when   since   but   and   then

She was going out to play. It rained. ....

....

He went to the cinema. He saw an adventure film. ....

....

We decided to go to the beach. The sun shone. ....

....

My friend came round. We were able to play together. ....

....

You came to visit me. I was ill. ....

....

Write sentences of your own, and use the conjunctions left over from the exercise above.

....

....

....

....

....

Calligrams

Do you know what a **calligram** is? Here is part of one.

A **calligram** is a type of **shape poem**. It uses the way the letters are written or printed to add to the meaning of the words.

A **calligram** about cold weather could have writing that looks shaky.

A **calligram** is a type of **shape poem**. It uses the way the letters are written or printed to add to the meaning of the words.

Try writing your own **calligram** here.

Answer Section with Parents' Notes

Key Stage 2
Ages 7–8

This 8-page section provides answers or explanatory notes to all the activities in this book. This will enable you to assess your child's work.

Point out any spelling mistakes, incorrect punctuation and grammatical errors as you mark each page. Also correct any handwriting errors. (Your child should use the handwriting style taught at his or her school.) As well as making corrections, it is very important to praise your child's efforts and achievements.

Encourage your child to use a dictionary, and suggest that he or she uses a notebook to compile a **word bank** of new words or difficult spellings.

---

2 ☆ Prefixes

Can you reassemble the words below by adding a **prefix** to each **root word**? D
Remember: A **prefix** is a group of letters added to the beginning of a word to change its meaning.

ex-   mis-   co-   non-   anti-

take   ordinate
freeze
lead   change   behave
port   clockwise
place   fiction   tend
operate

mis- _misbehave, mistake, mislead, misplace_

non- _non-fiction_

ex- _export, extend, exchange_

co- _coordinate, cooperate_

anti- _anticlockwise, antifreeze_

Can you make any more words by using the same **prefixes** with different **root words**? D

....

.... Answers may vary ....

....

Remember: Add any new words to your **word bank**.

This activity helps your child to recognise prefixes, a skill that will develop spelling and vocabulary. Encourage the use of a dictionary in the second exercise; this will help your child make a wide range of words out of prefixes and root words.

---

3 ☆ Writing a shape poem

Here is a shape **poem**.

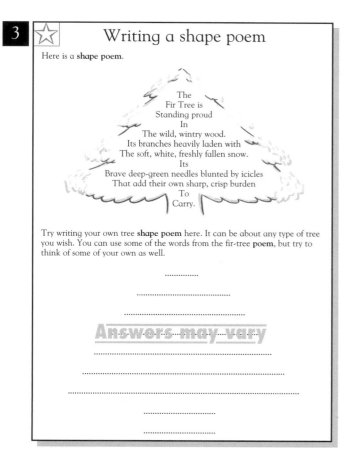

The
Fir Tree is
Standing proud
In
The wild, wintry wood.
Its branches heavily laden with
The soft, white, freshly fallen snow.
Its
Brave deep-green needles blunted by icicles
That add their own sharp, crisp burden
To
Carry.

Try writing your own tree **shape poem** here. It can be about any type of tree you wish. You can use some of the words from the fir-tree **poem**, but try to think of some of your own as well.

....

....

....

Answers may vary

....

....

....

....

Try to encourage your child to produce an original shape poem. It might help to write about a tree your child is familiar with. Talk about the tree together. If your child has difficulties, suggest that he or she rewrite the featured poem in his or her own words.

---

4 ☆ Homophones

Use a dictionary to find the definition of each of the **homophones** below. Then use each **homophone** in a separate sentence. D
Remember: Homophones are words that sound the same but have a different meaning and sometimes a different spelling.

pair ....
pear ....
pare ....

write ....
right ....

bear ....
bare ....

read ....
reed ....

to ....
too ....
two ....

Remember: Add any new words to your **word bank**.

This activity reinforces your child's understanding of homophones by asking him or her to make up sentences that include homophones. Accept any sentences that are grammatically correct and that use each word in the correct context .

Multiple meanings

Here is a word that has at least three **meanings**.

> **wave** means: a gesture
> to sway
> a moving ridge of water

Find one word, or **homograph**, to fit the three **meanings** in each group.
Remember: A **homograph** is a word with the same **spelling** as another word but with a different meaning.

opposite of left
correct
a true claim _right_

without a pattern
a flat piece of land
easily understood _plain_

a small sticker on a letter
a mark
to bring down your foot hard _stamp_

a group with members
a caveman's weapon
a type of playing card _club_

part of a dress that trails along
to teach
a form of transport _train_

a long-legged bird
to stretch to see
a lifting machine _crane_

a game ending in a tie
to make pictures
to attract _draw_

a tool for opening doors
a list of map symbols
a scale of musical notes _key_

You may need to explain further the difference between homographs and homophones. Homographs share the same spelling but have different meanings; homophones share the same sound but have different meanings.

Using a dictionary

The **dictionary** tells you:
- a word's **meaning**
- how the word is **used** (*n.* = noun, *adj.* = adjective, *v.* = verb)
- the **origins** of the word (where it comes from)

All this information helps you remember how a word is spelt.

Look up the words below in your **dictionary**. Give as much information as you can about each word's **meanings**, **uses** and **origins**. D

act meanings: ....
uses: ....
origins: ....

boom meanings: ....
uses: ....
origins: ....

comic meanings: ....
uses: ....
origins: ....

dart meanings: ....
uses: ....
origins: ....

electric meanings: ....
uses: ....
origins: ....

Answers may vary

The next four pages help familiarise your child with the wealth of information in a dictionary. Answers will vary depending on the dictionary used. Your child may need help if the dictionary is very detailed or simple. Accept any reasonably researched answers.

Using a dictionary

To make it easier to find a single word in a big **dictionary**, think of the book as being divided into four **quarters**, like this:

First quarter: A, B, C, D, E, F
Second quarter: G, H, I, J, K, L, M
Third quarter: N, O, P, Q, R, S
Fourth quarter: _T, U, V, W, X, Y, Z_

Did you notice any words amongst the scrambled letters on page 4? There are ten words for you to find. Make a list of these words and where they belong in the **dictionary** – in the first, second, third or fourth **quarter**?

vole	_fourth quarter_
devil	_first quarter_
dame	_first quarter_
lime	_second quarter_
ten	_fourth quarter_
thing	_fourth quarter_
ton	_fourth quarter_
won	_fourth quarter_
cone	_first quarter_
nap	_third quarter_

Remember: Add any new words to your **word bank**.

Quick recognition of the letters of the alphabet and their order in the four quarters of the dictionary will help your child to look up words more easily and will assist with his or her spelling and reading skills.

Alphabetical order

List the words below in **alphabetical order**. Then write down their **meanings**, **uses** and **origins**. You will need to continue on page 9. D

quack   yarn   zip   part   sandwich
watch   rear   unit   note   xylophone
object   tank   volume

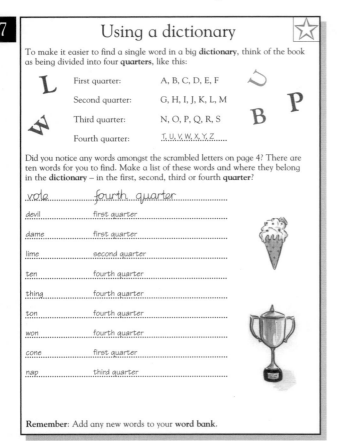

note meanings: ....
uses: ....
origins: ....

object meanings: ....
uses: ....
origins: ....

part meanings: ....
uses: ....
origins: ....

quack meanings: ....
uses: ....
origins: ....

rear meanings: ....
uses: ....
origins: ....

sandwich meanings: ....
uses: ....
origins: ....

Answers may vary

See notes for page 6. The exercise on pages 8 and 9 provides further dictionary practice. Take this chance to look at a dictionary with your child. It may help if you explain the parts of an entry, discussing plurals, pronunciation guides, abbreviations and definitions.

tank — meanings: .... uses: .... origins: ....

unit — meanings: .... uses: .... origins: ....

volume — meanings: .... uses: .... origins: ....

watch — meanings: .... uses: .... origins: ....

xylophone — meanings: .... uses: .... origins: ....

yarn — meanings: .... uses: .... origins: ....

zip — meanings: .... uses: .... origins: ....

See notes for page 6. Look at the alphabetical order in a dictionary with your child. Talk about how it lists words that start with the same letter, then uses the second, third or fourth letter of each word to decide which word appears first.

Writing about talking

Read this extract from the **legend** *King Arthur*. The brave King Arthur has been badly wounded. He wants the knight Bedivere to help him.

They took Arthur inside and laid him down to rest.
"Bedivere," rasped the king, "take my sword, Excalibur. Throw it into the lake. Then come back and tell me what you have seen."
Bedivere took Excalibur. Never in his life had he held such an exquisite sword. He could not bear to throw away such a treasure, so he hid it under a tree, then hurried back to Arthur.
"Did you do it?" Arthur asked him.
"I did, sir."
"And what did you see?"
"Nothing but the waves and the wind, my lord."
"Then you have lied to me!" cried Arthur. "Do as I commanded."
Bedivere went back to the lake. Again he admired Excalibur's unearthly beauty, again he hid it, again he lied to his king.
Arthur was growing weaker. "By Heaven," he gasped, "if you do not obey, there will be no future ...." He could speak no more.
Bedivere was moved by the mystery of his words. Without a word he strode back to the lake shore. This time he took Excalibur and threw it with all his strength, out into the middle of the lake.
At once, a hand rose out of the swirling waters, caught the sword, and brandished it three times. Then, out of the mist, silken voices began to chant:
"Bring him for healing, Over the water!"
Bedivere shivered. He turned and ran back to his wounded lord.
"Quick!" he called to Sir Lucan. "We must fetch the king!"

From King Arthur, retold by Rosalind Kerven

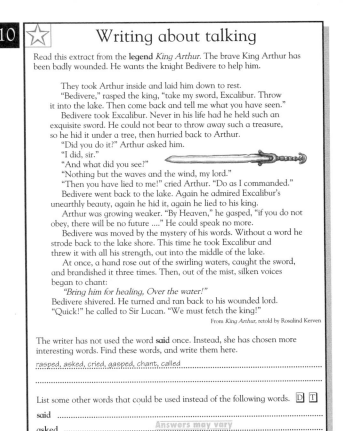

The writer has not used the word **said** once. Instead, she has chosen more interesting words. Find these words, and write them here.

rasped, asked, cried, gasped, chant, called

List some other words that could be used instead of the following words. ☐ ☐

said ....

asked ....

This activity encourages your child to find examples of dialogue markers, such as *asked* and *called*. Talk about how the writer has used different dialogue markers to add interest. A dictionary and thesaurus will help in finding more dialogue markers.

A mysterious story poem

Read this **poem** aloud.

The Listeners

"Is there anybody there?" said the Traveller,
Knocking on the moonlit door;
And his horse in the silence champed the grasses
Of the forest's ferny floor:
And a bird flew up out of the turret,
Above the Traveller's head:
And he smote upon the door again a second time;
"Is there anybody there?" he said.
But no one descended to the Traveller;
No head from the leaf-fringed sill
Leaned over and looked into his grey eyes,
Where he stood perplexed and still.
But only a host of phantom listeners
That dwelt in the lone house then
Stood listening in the quiet of the moonlight
To that voice from the world of men:
Stood thronging the faint moonbeams on the dark stair,
That goes down to the empty hall,
Hearkening in an air stirred and shaken
By the lonely Traveller's call.
And he felt in his heart their strangeness,
Their stillness answering his cry,
While his horse moved, cropping the dark turf,
'Neath the starred and leafy sky;
For he suddenly smote on the door, even
Louder, and lifted his head: –
"Tell them I came, and no one answered,
That I kept my word," he said.
Never the least stir made the listeners,
Though every word he spake
Fell echoing through the shadowiness of the still house
From the one man left awake:
Ay, they heard his foot upon the stirrup,
And the sound of iron on stone,
And how the silence surged softly backward,
When the plunging hoofs were gone.

Walter de la Mare

This **poem** seems to be part of a longer mystery story. Why is it mysterious?
The poem seems mysterious because neither the Traveller nor the reader know why the people who live in the house are not there.

Listen to your child read the poem, helping where necessary with any difficult words. Encourage him or her to reread the poem, this time thinking about its meaning. Accept any answer that can be justified by some aspect of the poem.

Understanding the poem

Answer these questions about the **poem** called *The Listeners* on page 11.

Where does this part of the story happen?
This part of the story happens by a house in a forest.

When does it happen (day or night)? Which words tell you this?
It happens at night. The words moonlit, moonlight, moonbeams, dark, starred, shadowiness and left awake tell me so.

In your opinion, who or what are "The Listeners"?
The Listeners are ghosts.

The Traveller speaks in this **poem**. What are his words?
"Is there anybody there?"
"Tell them I came, and no one answered, That I kept my word."

How does the first line of the **poem** make you feel?
The first line makes me feel curious to know if anybody is there.

What do you notice about the sounds in the third and fourth lines,
And his horse in the silence champed the grasses
Of the forest's ferny floor
and what does this tell you about the horse's behaviour?
There are a lot of 's' and 'f' sounds in the third and fourth lines. The horse's eating made soft sounds in the quiet night.

Make a list of the **adjectives** that are used to describe the Traveller.
Remember: An **adjective** is a describing word.

grey (eyes), perplexed, still, lonely

The questions on this page encourage your child to look at the words of the poem carefully and help him or her to develop comprehension skills. Some answers require a subjective response and are acceptable as long as they can be justified.

13 — Understanding the poem

Answer these further questions about the **poem** on page 11.

Find the meanings of the old-fashioned words in the **poem**. Then write down why you think the poet chose these words. [D]

smote – hit; dwelt – lived; hearkening – listening; 'neath – beneath; spake – spoke; ay – always. The poet chose these words because they give the poem a sense of something happening long ago. *Answers may vary*

Read the **poem** again, looking at the lines and listening for the **rhymes**. How would you describe the **rhyming pattern**?

The poem has a regular pattern of rhyming pairs. Every second line rhymes. *Answers may vary*

Count the **syllables** in the first eight lines – can you find a **rhythmic pattern**? What is it?
Remember: A **syllable** is a word or part of a word that is one beat long.

The poem follows a rhythmic pattern of a long line followed by a shorter line.

Writing practice
Choose a section from the **poem** and write it here.
Remember: Join your letters carefully and space your words evenly.
Begin new lines in the same places as in the printed **poem**.

Answers may vary

These exercises relate to the poem on page 11. Defining old words can help improve dictionary skills. Looking at the rhyme and rhythm reveals the poem's structure. Check that your child has copied a section correctly, and check his or her handwriting.

14 — Pronouns

Pronouns are used instead of **nouns** to avoid repeating the **nouns** themselves. Read the following text, which has no **pronouns** in it.

The Traveller arrived at the door. The Traveller knocked on the door, but there was no answer, so the Traveller knocked again. Meanwhile, the Traveller's horse was grazing. The Traveller's horse seemed untroubled.

With **pronouns**, the text becomes much less repetitive.

The Traveller arrived at the door. **He** knocked on **it**, but there was no answer, so **he** knocked again. Meanwhile, **his** horse was grazing. **It** seemed untroubled.

Go back to the **poem** on page 11, and underline all the **pronouns** you can find.

Rewrite the following sentences changing the **nouns** in bold type to **pronouns**.

The Traveller rode **the Traveller's** horse as fast as **the horse** could go.

The Traveller rode his horse as fast as it could go.

Emma said that **Emma** wanted to read **Emma's** favourite poem to them.

Emma said that she wanted to read her favourite poem to them.

Jack and Kate enjoyed the poem that **Emma** read to **Jack and Kate**.

They enjoyed the poem that she read to them.

This exercise helps your child identify pronouns and their functions. If your child has difficulty with this exercise, make a list of the various pronouns together. Ask him or her to reread the sentences and tell you which words are pronouns.

15 — Conjunctions

Conjunctions are words that join sentences. Choose one **conjunction** from the list below to join each pair of sentences. Use a different **conjunction** each time.

if   so   while   although   because   when   since   but   and   then

She was going out to play. It rained. She was going out to play but it rained.

He went to the cinema. He saw an adventure film. He went to the cinema and he saw an adventure film.

We decided to go to the beach. The sun shone. We decided to go to the beach while the sun shone.

My friend came round. We were able to play together. My friend came round so we were able to play together.

You came to visit me. I was ill. You came to visit me when I was ill.

Answers may vary

Write sentences of your own, and use the conjunctions left over from the exercise above.

Answers may vary

This page focuses on conjunctions and their functions. Encourage your child to have fun trying different conjunctions between sentences. If he or she chooses a conjunction that doesn't make sense, talk about why another fits better. Accept any sensible answers.

16 — Calligrams

Do you know what a **calligram** is? Here is part of one.

A **calligram** is a type of **shape poem**. It uses the way the letters are written or printed to add to the meaning of the words.

A **calligram** about cold weather could have writing that looks shaky.

Try writing your own **calligram** here.

Answers may vary

Discuss different ideas for a calligram with your child. Encourage your child to have fun with this exercise and to enjoy thinking up suitable words. The appearance and shape of the words in the poem should suggest the subject in some way.

17 Changing words with apostrophes ☆

Do you know how to use an **apostrophe** to shorten words? Try shortening these words. The first one has been done for you. Remember, an apostrophe is used to show that one or more letters are missing.

could not	couldn't
I will	I'll
he will	he'll
she will	she'll
might not	mightn't
would not	wouldn't
do not	don't

Now write out these **shortened words** in full without using an **apostrophe**.

mustn't	must not
shouldn't	should not
we'll	we will
we're	we are
aren't	are not
it'll	it will
you'll	you will
couldn't	could not
didn't	did not

This page reinforces understanding of how an apostrophe is used to show the position of missing letters when two words are joined to make one word. Your child may find it useful to know that such shortened words are called *contractions*.

18 ☆ Proof-reading

Here is a **conversation** that includes two **riddles**. Some of the **capital letters**, **commas**, **speech marks** and some other **punctuation marks** have been left out. **Proof-read** the text, and write your corrections on the page.

"Do you like riddles?" asked Joshua. "When I can solve them," replied Sue. "Try this one then," Joshua continued.

"This thing eats up all we know,
Animals, plants and birds also.
It bites metal, grinds rocks down,
Attacks the man who wears the crown.
Lofty mountains are made lower
By its never ceasing power."

"That's difficult!" complained Sue. "You'll have to give me time." "That's it!" laughed Joshua. "You've said the answer!" Sue thought for a moment. "So I have!" she exclaimed. "My turn now."

"A box without hinges, key or lid,
Yet golden treasure inside is hid."

Riddles adapted from *The Hobbit* by J. R. R. Tolkien

Write the answers to the two **riddles** here.

The answer to Joshua's **riddle** is _time._

The answer to Sue's **riddle** is _an egg._

These exercises test punctuation. Discuss any differences between your child's answers and those shown above. Your child may come up with other answers – accept these answers if he or she can justify them and shows an understanding of what a riddle is.

19 ☆ Editing

Sometimes we need to **shorten** or **change** sentences to make them quicker and easier to read. Here are some sentences that were spoken. Cross out all the unnecessary words. Then rewrite the remaining words as simply as you can. Make sure the meaning is not lost and that you still have complete sentences.

> Apples for cider are ~~really~~ not ~~very~~ sweet ~~at all and~~ you can see them ~~all~~ growing in ~~these cider~~ orchards, ~~generally speaking,~~ in the south-west of England.

Sour cider apples are grown in orchards in south-west England

> If you ever wondered why apples have all those bits inside, then I can tell you that the pips are actually the seeds and I can also tell you that the core, which was part of the apple blossom, holds the seeds so that more apple trees can grow and so on.

Answers may vary

> If you want to make a really good job of saying a poem out loud to other people, you actually need to learn the words and everything really well and remember them in your head or you will forget what you are doing and it will not be very thrilling for the people who are listening to it.

Answers may vary

This activity gives practice in summarising text and in sentence recognition. Your child should write well-formed sentences that provide all the basic information but that leave out unnecessary or repetitive words and phrases.

20 ☆ Presenting information

Read this **recipe**.

Speedy Pizza for Two
For the sauce: 1 onion, 1 small can tomatoes, 2 teaspoons tomato paste, a pinch of salt, a pinch of pepper. **For the dough**: 150 g self-raising flour, 3–4 tablespoons milk, 3 tablespoons butter, a pinch of salt. **For the topping**: 50 g grated cheese, 6 mushrooms.

1. To make the dough, put the flour, butter and salt into a bowl and add the milk a little at a time, mixing well, until the dough is smooth.
2. First, turn on the oven to 220°C to warm up.
3. Cook the sauce mixture over a low heat for 15 minutes, stirring it from time to time.
4. Place the circles of dough on a greased baking tray, then spread the sauce evenly over each circle.
5. Divide the dough in half, and roll out each half into a circular shape.
6. Put the pizzas in the oven to cook for 15–20 minutes.
7. To make the sauce, chop the onion and mix it in a saucepan with the tomatoes, tomato paste, salt and pepper.
8. Top the pizzas with sliced mushrooms and grated cheese.

The order of the **instructions** is wrong. Write them out here in the correct order.

1. First, turn on the oven to 220°C to warm up.
2. To make the sauce, chop the onion and mix it in a saucepan with the tomatoes, tomato paste, salt and pepper.
3. Cook the sauce mixture over a low heat for 15 minutes, stirring it from time to time.
4. To make the dough, put the flour, butter and salt into a bowl and add the milk a little at a time, mixing well, until the dough is smooth.
5. Divide the dough in half, and roll out each half into a circular shape.
6. Place the circles of dough on a greased baking tray, then spread the sauce evenly over each circle.
7. Top the pizzas with sliced mushrooms and grated cheese.
8. Put the pizzas in the oven to cook for 15–20 minutes.

On this page, your child has more practice investigating factual information and also learns about the importance of writing instructions in a logical order. Take a close look at your child's handwriting, and praise your child's efforts.

Compound words

The word **jigsaw** is made up of two words put together (jig + saw).
Can you pair up these **jigsaw** pieces to make other **compound words**?
Remember: A compound word is a word made up of two other words.

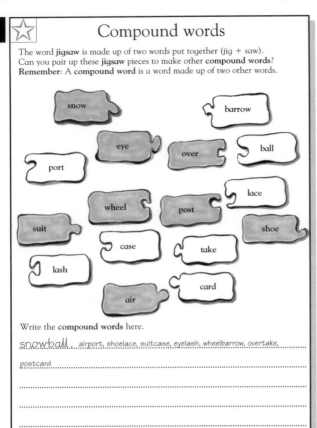

snow
eye
over
port
wheel
post
suit
case
lash
air
barrow
ball
lace
shoe
take
card

Write the **compound words** here.

snowball   airport, shoelace, suitcase, eyelash, wheelbarrow, overtake,

postcard

Check that your child has paired up the correct
words. Use this opportunity to look carefully at
your child's handwriting. If appropriate, point out
any areas that need further practice.

What's important to you?

Read this **poem** aloud.

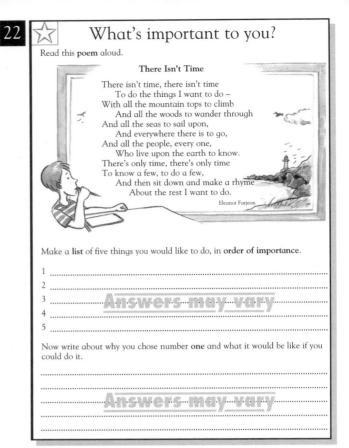

There Isn't Time

There isn't time, there isn't time
    To do the things I want to do –
With all the mountain tops to climb
    And all the woods to wander through
And all the seas to sail upon,
    And everywhere there is to go,
And all the people, every one,
    Who live upon the earth to know.
There's only time, there's only time
    To know a few, to do a few,
    And then sit down and make a rhyme
    About the rest I want to do.

Eleanor Farjeon

Make a **list** of five things you would like to do, in **order of importance**.

1 ....
2 ....
3 .... Answers may vary ....
4 ....
5 ....

Now write about why you chose number **one** and what it would be like if you
could do it.

....
....
.... Answers may vary ....

This activity gives your child the opportunity to
practise listing skills by arranging in order of
importance the things he or she would like to do.
Encourage your child to explain why his or her
first choice is the most important.

Marking time

Read this text and then answer the question below.

Text A: The Part-time Time-traveller

You may find this hard to believe, but **I once** built a time machine.
It was made from scrap, which I collected **when** I visited the local
recycling centre **at weekends**.
    First of all, I found some old bicycle parts, including a real leather
saddle, which you don't often see **nowadays**.
    A week later, I picked up a huge electric clock, which I had seen
years ago in the bus station (**before** clocks went digital).
    Meanwhile, I had a real stroke of luck …

All the words in **bold type** are doing a similar job. Explain what it is here.
The words in bold type tell us when things happen.
....

Now read this text.

Text B: The Part-time Time-traveller

George used to visit the local recycling centre
at weekends. He was always rifling through the scrap
for old bicycle parts and other interesting things.
His neighbours thought that he was a bit strange.
    One weekend, he was seen struggling home with
a horribly heavy old clock that some said had come from
the bus station ten years previously.
    Then things turned really peculiar …

Both the texts above tell the same story but in different ways. Explain the
difference between text A and text B.

Text A is in the first person. The subject is I.

Text B is in the third person. The subject is George.

The first exercise tests recognition of words about "when"
events happened. In the second exercise, accept answers
that imply the texts are written from different viewpoints.
Explain that Text A is in the first person and Text B is in
the third person if your child does not know these terms.

Labelling a diagram

Reread the texts on page 23. Now draw a **diagram** of George's "Time Machine"
as you imagine it. **Label** each part of the machine, saying what it is made
from and what it does.

Remember: A label consists of a few words, or even just one word, that tell
people about a particular part of a diagram.

Answers may vary

By making a labelled diagram of George's "Time
Machine", your child is learning another way to
communicate information. Encourage your child
to talk in detail about the different parts of the
"Time Machine" that he or she has labelled.

Planning your own story

Look over your work on pages 23 and 24. **Where** is the story of *The Part-time Time Traveller* **set**, and how did it **begin**? How would you **finish** the story? **Plan** your story on this page by writing short **notes**.
Remember: You do not need to use full sentences when writing **notes**.

Characters: ....

....

Setting: ....

Beginning: ....

....

....

What happens: ....

....

....

....

....

....

....

Ending: ....

....

....

Learning how to plan a story will improve your child's writing and increase his or her confidence. When checking the plan, make sure that he or she understands that full sentences and "best" handwriting are not needed when making notes.

Writing your story

Look over the **notes** you wrote on page 25, then write your story here. Use **paragraphs**, and fit your story into the pattern set out for you. Continue your story on page 27.

Either start with:
You may find this hard to believe, but I once built a time machine. It was made from scrap …
or
George used to visit the local recycling centre at weekends. He was always rifling through the scrap …

The Part-time Time-traveller

Start here: ....

....

....

....

....

What happens: ....

....

....

....

....

This activity gives story-writing practice. Compare your child's story to the notes in the previous exercise, and ask about any changes made. Make sure your child has kept to the first or third person. Check that paragraphs have been used correctly.

Continuing your story

....

....

....

....

....

....

....

....

....

....

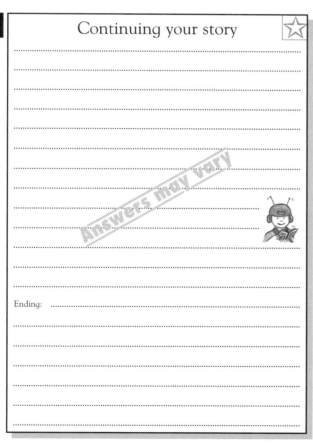

....

....

Ending: ....

....

....

....

....

See notes for page 26. As you read your child's story, check that the basic sentence structures are correct, look for linked ideas, imaginative expression and appropriate or interesting words. Praise the aspects of your child's story that you like.

Back-cover blurbs

Here is the **blurb** from the back cover of a book.

Told and retold down the centuries, the stories of King Arthur and the Knights of the Round Table have enthralled generation after generation. This *Eyewitness Classic* edition, with its innovative use of photography and narrative illustration, makes it possible for children to enjoy the real world of the Arthur legend.

Look back at page 10 to find the **title** and **author** of the book. Write them here.

King Arthur retold by Rosalind Kerven

If you have read this book, you could use it for the next piece of work. If not, choose a **fiction** book you have read recently. Write your own back cover **blurb** in the book below. Your **blurb** should encourage people of your age to read the book.
Remember: Fiction means a story invented by the writer or speaker.

.... (title)

.... (author)

Check that your child understands that a blurb is a short review on a book's back cover, and that he or she knows where to find a book's title and author. The blurb should be concise, interesting or exciting and give an idea of what the book is about.

A book review

Use the guide below to help you write a **book review** of a **fiction** book you have read recently.

Title: .... Author: ....

(Complete in full, using capital letters as necessary.)

Main characters: (only the most important people)

....

....

Story: (brief outline only – but in the right order)

....

....

....

Opinions: (your own views)

Plot: (what happens – is it believable, exciting, etc?)

....

....

....

Characters: (Do they seem real? Do you like or dislike them?)

....

....

....

Language: (Did the words do their job well?)

....

....

....

Answers may vary

Writing a book review encourages your child to use concise language and to recognise the key details in a story. Look for clear and interesting expression and reasons for the opinions given. Don't forget to praise your child's efforts.

Getting the message

Letter 1

Dear Sir,
 I would be interested to know whether any other readers have noticed the strange lights in the night sky.
 For the last week, I have woken at midnight to see flashing green lights hovering over the park.

Yours faithfully,
N. O. Sleep
Smalltown

Letter 2

4 Daffodil Street,
Smalltown.
Wednesday

Dear Mum,
 Just a quick note to say that I'm okay here. Aunty Liz sends her love and is looking forward to seeing you and Dad on Saturday. Met an alien from the 22nd century last night. Hope you are both well – see you soon!
Love,
Kirsty

Letter 3

About A.D. 2000
Planet Earth

Landed smoothly at 25.00 hours.
No problems with machine, but need warmer clothing.
Hope you like the picture – it's a form of time meter used here!

Greetings,
Zop

Can you tell who wrote these three letters? Put the correct number by each description below.

a child's letter home ....2.........................

an alien's postcard home ....3.........................

a letter to a local newspaper ...1.........................

This page tests your child's recognition of different types of letters. If he or she has difficulty, read each letter together, pointing out the clues to the identity of the writer – look at where the letter was sent from and who received it, as well as its content and style.

Writing notes

Reread the letters on page 30. Something unusual has been going on in Smalltown! Kirsty made some quick **notes** about what happened when she met a time-travelling alien from the 22nd century. Imagine what these **notes** might say, and write them here.
Remember: You don't need to use full sentences when writing **notes**.

Woke up at midnight

....

....

....

....

....

....

....

....

....

....

....

....

....

Answers may vary

This activity gives your child more practice in making notes and encourages imaginative expression. Check that he or she understands that full sentences are not necessary for writing notes, and tell your child what you admire about his or her ideas.

Writing a letter

Reread the **notes** you wrote on page 31. Imagine that Kirsty is your sister, and write a letter to one of your friends about what Kirsty has told you.

(your address)
....

....

....

(today's date)
....

Dear .... ,

....

....

....

....

....

Your friend,

....

Answers may vary

This exercise will help your child to practise letter-writing skills. Encourage him or her to use the notes made on page 31. Discuss the layout of the letter, and make sure it includes an address, a date and your child's signature.

Changing words with apostrophes

Do you know how to use an **apostrophe** to shorten words? Try shortening these words. The first one has been done for you. Remember, an apostrophe is used to show that one or more letters are missing.

could not   *couldn't* ....

I will   ....

he will   ....

she will   ....

might not   ....

would not   ....

do not   ....

Now write out these **shortened words** in full without using an **apostrophe**.

mustn't   *must not* ....

shouldn't   ....

we'll   ....

we're   ....

aren't   ....

it'll   ....

you'll   ....

couldn't   ....

didn't   ....

Proof-reading

Here is a **conversation** that includes two **riddles**. Some of the **capital letters**, **commas**, **speech marks** and some other **punctuation marks** have been left out. **Proof-read** the text, and write your corrections on the page.

Do you like riddles   asked joshua   When I can solve them   replied sue   Try this one then   joshua continued

This thing eats up all we know
Animals   plants and birds also
It bites metal   grinds rocks down
Attacks the man who wears the crown.
Lofty mountains are made lower
By its never ceasing power.

That's difficult   complained sue   you'll have to give me time That's it   laughed joshua   you've said the answer sue thought for a moment   so i have   she exclaimed My turn now.

A box without hinges   key or lid
Yet golden treasure inside is hid.

Riddles adapted from *The Hobbit* by J. R. R. Tolkien

Write the answers to the two **riddles** here.

The answer to Joshua's **riddle** is ....

The answer to Sue's **riddle** is ....

Editing

Sometimes we need to **shorten** or **change** sentences to make them quicker and easier to read. Here are some sentences that were spoken. Cross out all the unnecessary words. Then rewrite the remaining words as simply as you can. Make sure the meaning is not lost and that you still have complete sentences.

> Apples for cider are ~~really~~ not ~~very~~ sweet ~~at all and~~ you can see them ~~all~~ growing in ~~these cider~~ orchards, ~~generally speaking~~, in the south-west of England.

Sour cider apples are grown in orchards in south-west England.

> If you ever wondered why apples have all those bits inside, then I can tell you that the pips are actually the seeds and I can also tell you that the core, which was part of the apple blossom, holds the seeds so that more apple trees can grow and so on.

....

....

....

> If you want to make a really good job of saying a poem out loud to other people, you actually need to learn the words and everything really well and remember them in your head or you will forget what you are doing and it will not be very thrilling for the people who are listening to it.

....

....

....

19

Presenting information

Read this **recipe**.

Speedy Pizza for Two

For the sauce: 1 onion, 1 small can tomatoes, 2 teaspoons tomato paste, a pinch of salt, a pinch of pepper. **For the dough**: 150 g self-raising flour, 3–4 tablespoons milk, 3 tablespoons butter, a pinch of salt. **For the topping**: 50 g grated cheese, 6 mushrooms.

1   To make the dough, put the flour, butter and salt into a bowl and add the milk a little at a time, mixing well, until the dough is smooth.
2   First, turn on the oven to 220°C to warm up.
3   Cook the sauce mixture over a low heat for 15 minutes, stirring it from time to time.
4   Place the circles of dough on a greased baking tray, then spread the sauce evenly over each circle.
5   Divide the dough in half, and roll out each half into a circular shape.
6   Put the pizzas in the oven to cook for 15–20 minutes.
7   To make the sauce, chop the onion and mix it in a saucepan with the tomatoes, tomato paste, salt and pepper.
8   Top the pizzas with sliced mushrooms and grated cheese.

The order of the **instructions** is wrong. Write them out here in the correct order.

1 ....

2 ....
....

3 ....
....

4 ....
....

5 ....

6 ....
....

7 ....

8 ....

Compound words

The word **jigsaw** is made up of two words put together (jig + saw).
Can you pair up these **jigsaw** pieces to make other **compound words**?
Remember: A **compound word** is a word made up of two other words.

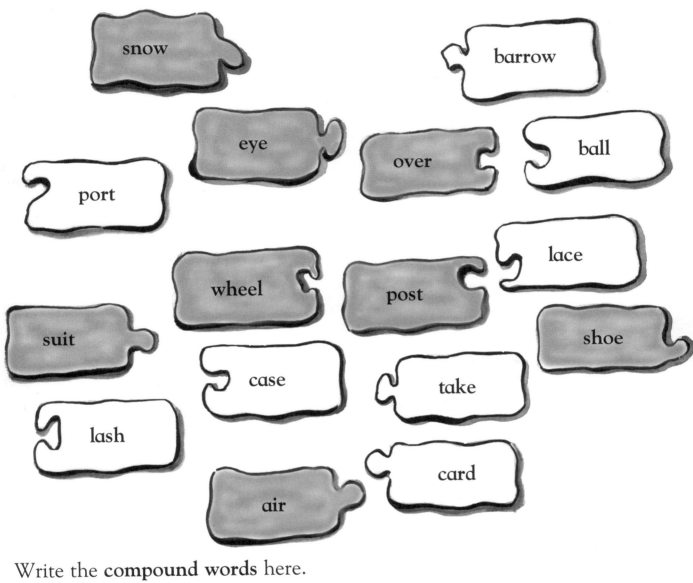

Write the **compound words** here.

snowball

What's important to you?

Read this **poem** aloud.

There Isn't Time

There isn't time, there isn't time
    To do the things I want to do –
With all the mountain tops to climb
    And all the woods to wander through
And all the seas to sail upon,
    And everywhere there is to go,
And all the people, every one,
    Who live upon the earth to know.
There's only time, there's only time
To know a few, to do a few,
    And then sit down and make a rhyme
    About the rest I want to do.

Eleanor Farjeon

Make a **list** of five things you would like to do, in **order of importance**.

1 ....

2 ....

3 ....

4 ....

5 ....

Now write about why you chose number **one** and what it would be like if you could do it.

....

....

....

....

....

Marking time

Read this text and then answer the question below.

Text A: The Part-time Time-traveller

You may find this hard to believe, but **I once** built a time machine. It was made from scrap, which I collected **when** I visited the local recycling centre **at weekends**.

First of all, I found some old bicycle parts, including a real leather saddle, which you don't often see **nowadays**.

A week later, I picked up a huge electric clock, which I had seen **years ago** in the bus station (**before** clocks went digital).

Meanwhile, I had a real stroke of luck …

All the words in **bold type** are doing a similar job. Explain what it is here.

....

....

Now read this text.

Text B: The Part-time Time-traveller

George used to visit the local recycling centre at weekends. He was always rifling through the scrap for old bicycle parts and other interesting things. His neighbours thought that he was a bit strange.

One weekend, he was seen struggling home with a horribly heavy old clock that some said had come from the bus station ten years previously.

Then things turned really peculiar …

Both the texts above tell the same story but in different ways. Explain the difference between text A and text B.

....

....

....

Labelling a diagram

Reread the texts on page 23. Now draw a **diagram** of George's "Time Machine" as you imagine it. **Label** each part of the machine, saying what it is made from and what it does.

Remember: A **label** consists of a few words, or even just one word, that tell people about a particular part of a diagram.

Planning your own story

Look over your work on pages 23 and 24. **Where** is the story of *The Part-time Time Traveller* **set**, and how did it **begin**? How would you **finish** the story?
Plan your story on this page by writing short **notes**.
Remember: You do not need to use full sentences when writing **notes**.

Characters: ....

....

Setting: ....

Beginning: ....

....

....

What happens: ....

....

....

....

....

....

....

....

Ending: ....

....

....

Writing your story

Look over the **notes** you wrote on page 25, then write your story here.
Use **paragraphs**, and fit your story into the pattern set out for you. Continue
your story on page 27.

Either start with:

*You may find this hard to believe, but I once
built a time machine. It was made from scrap …*

or

*George used to visit the local recycling centre
at weekends. He was always rifling through the scrap …*

The Part-time Time-traveller

Start here: ....

....

....

....

....

What happens: ....

....

....

....

....

....

....

Continuing your story

....

....

....

....

....

....

....

....

....

Ending: ....

....

....

....

Back-cover blurbs

Here is the **blurb** from the back cover of a book.

    Told and retold down the centuries, the stories of King Arthur and the Knights of the Round Table have enthralled generation after generation. This *Eyewitness Classic* edition, with its innovative use of photography and narrative illustration, makes it possible for children to enjoy the real world of the Arthur legend.

Look back at page 10 to find the **title** and **author** of the book.
Write them here.

....

If you have read this book, you could use it for the next piece of work.
If not, choose a **fiction** book you have read recently. Write your own back cover **blurb** in the book below. Your **blurb** should encourage people of your age to read the book.
Remember: **Fiction** means a story invented by the writer or speaker.

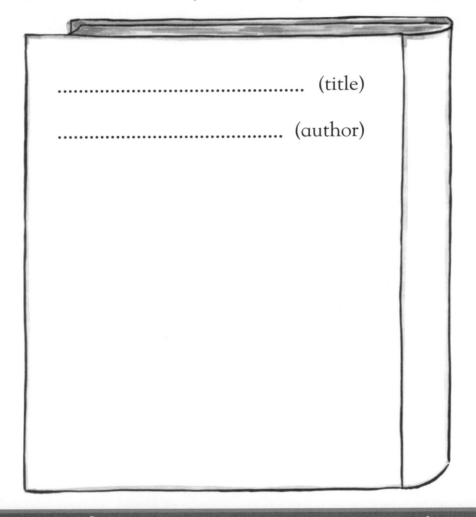

.... (title)

.... (author)

A book review

Use the guide below to help you write a **book review** of a **fiction** book you have read recently.

Title: .... **Author**: ....
(Complete in full, using capital letters as necessary.)

Main characters: (only the most important people)

....

....

Story: (brief outline only – but in the right order)

....

....

....

Opinions: (your own views)

Plot: (what happens – is it believable, exciting, etc?)

....

....

....

Characters: (Do they seem real? Do you like or dislike them?)

....

....

....

Language: (Did the words do their job well?)

....

....

....

Getting the message

Letter 1

Dear Sir,

    I would be interested to know whether any other readers have noticed the strange lights in the night sky.

    For the last week, I have woken at midnight to see flashing green lights hovering over the park.

Yours faithfully,
N. O. Sleep
Smalltown

Letter 2

4 Daffodil Street,
Smalltown.
Wednesday

Dear Mum,

    Just a quick note to say that I'm okay here. Aunty Liz sends her love and is looking forward to seeing you and Dad on Saturday. Met an alien from the 22nd century last night.

    Hope you are both well – see you soon!

Love,
Kirsty

Letter 3

About A.D. 2000
Planet Earth

Landed smoothly at 25.00 hours.
No problems with machine, but need warmer clothing.
Hope you like the picture – it's a form of time meter used here!

Greetings,
Zop

Can you tell who wrote these three letters? Put the correct number by each description below.

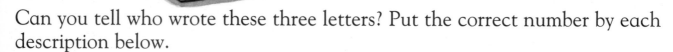

a child's letter home ....

an alien's postcard home ....

a letter to a local newspaper ....

Writing notes

Reread the letters on page 30. Something unusual has been going on in Smalltown! Kirsty made some quick **notes** about what happened when she met a time-travelling alien from the 22nd century. Imagine what these **notes** might say, and write them here.

Remember: You don't need to use full sentences when writing **notes**.

Woke up at midnight

Writing a letter

Reread the **notes** you wrote on page 31. Imagine that Kirsty is your sister, and write a letter to one of your friends about what Kirsty has told you.

(your address)

....

....

....

(today's date)

....

Dear ....,

....

....

....

....

....

....

....

....

Your friend,

....